Little Pilgrims in God's World

ACTIVITY BOOK

79908   4/11

A publication of
Christian Liberty Press
502 West Euclid Avenue
Arlington Heights, Illinois 60004
www.christianlibertypress.com

Developed from *Little Pilgrims in God's World* by Jeff and Stephanie Dennison
Layout and editing by Edward J. Shewan
Illustrations by Vic Lockman
Copyediting by Diane C. Olson
Cover images © DesignPics 2011
        Pete Stec, front cover
        Carson Ganci, back cover
Cover design by Bob Fine

Scripture references are conformed to The Holy Bible, New King James Version ©1982, Thomas Nelson, Inc., so that modern readers may gain greater comprehension of the Word of God.

ISBN 978-1-932971-56-9

Printed in the United States of America

Contents

How To Use the Textbook

Start by reading each lesson to your student; then have him write the answers to the questions on a separate sheet of paper or say them orally. At the end of each lesson you will find at least one activity, which will reinforce the lesson. Most of the activities can be found in this *Activity Book*. The activities are quite varied, sometimes involving coloring, cutting, building, writing, etc. There are also additional activities included with each lesson, depending on how much time one has and the interest level of the student.

All lessons have a recurring activity under **Something Else To Do** that uses the **Bible verses** found at the beginning of each lesson. Each lesson contains a Bible verse with some words in bold-faced type. The student may memorize those parts of the verse in bold-faced type. The Bible verses are also found at the back of this *Activity Book* beginning on page 93 and can be removed. A suggestion for the memorization of the verses is to punch a hole in the upper left-hand corner of each verse card and put a metal ring about an inch in diameter through it. Subsequent verses can then be added to the ring so that the student has them all together for further review.

Some lessons also contain activities under **Something Else To Do** that are optional and are intended to further reinforce the concepts introduced in the lesson. One such activity is playing the Memory Game using the **vocabulary words**, which the student will be shown throughout the book. The vocabulary words and definitions for the Memory Game can be found at the back of this *Activity Book* beginning on page 105. They may be removed and kept together for further use. The teacher may choose to use these cards as a fun way to learn the vocabulary words. Teacher and student can decide how many cards they want to use at a time, gradually adding more cards to the game once previous vocabulary words are mastered.

Finally, **Further Study** is an optional activity that is meant to be a platform to further research and study of people, places, and concepts. Often the Internet is recommended, including books and suggested visits to the library, museum, zoo, and so forth.

May the Lord Jesus Christ help the student gain an appreciation for the work of God in his heart, family, church, society, and world.

Jeff and Stephanie Dennison
April 2011

UNIT 1: *God's Special People*

LESSON 1 Activity

&❧ Color the picture of the Passover.

SOMETHING ELSE TO DO

- Memorize Hebrews 13:14 (NKJV).

  For here we have no continuing city, but we seek the one to come.

- Learn the meaning of the vocabulary word "holy" for the Memory Game.

LESSON 2 Activity

- Find pictures of people from different parts of the world, using old magazines or print pictures from the Internet. Cut the pictures out and glue them to a piece of construction paper or poster board. At the top of the paper, write John 3:16.

SOMETHING ELSE TO DO

- Learn Isaiah 1:4b (NKJV). Memorize the words in **bold**.

  [Israel has] forsaken the LORD; they have provoked to anger the Holy One of Israel; they have turned away backward.

LESSON 3 Activity

- Using a map, atlas, or the computer, find various countries around the world. Find the United States, Brazil, Egypt, China, and the United Kindom.*

SOMETHING ELSE TO DO

- Learn Galatians 3:26, 29 (NKJV). Memorize the words in **bold**.

  For you are all sons of God through faith in Christ Jesus.... And if you are Christ's, then you are Abraham's seed, and heirs according to the promise.

- Learn the meaning of the vocabulary word "pilgrim" for the Memory Game.

---

* See the world map on pages 114 and 115 of this *Activity Book*. You may remove these pages; cut off the right, white edge of page 114; and tape them together. Keep this map in a safe place to use for other activities in this course.

UNIT 2: *Creation*

LESSON 4 Activities

❧ Make a ball or "globe" using blue Play-Doh®. Use a flashlight to represent the light, and shine it on the "globe."

❧ Write God's name at the top of the "Trinity triangle" and include His jobs. (*Answers:* **Father** [*top line*], **create**, **command**)

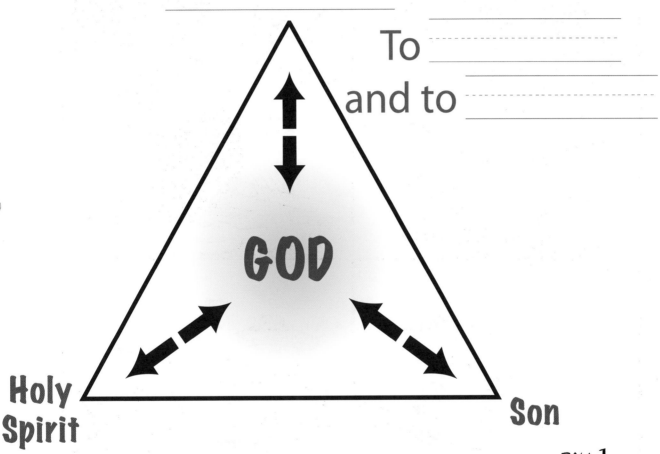

To _____

and to _____

❧ Turn to page 91 of this *Activity Book.* Find Day 1, and color the top half of the "world" yellow for the light and the bottom half black for the darkness for the timeline of creation.

SOMETHING ELSE TO DO

❧ Memorize Genesis 1:3 (NKJV).

Then God said, "Let there be light"; and there was light.

LESSON 5 Activities

❧ What are each of the children doing?
Put an "**X**" on the pictures that are examples of sin.

Go into a room, turn off all the lights, and close the blinds. If you have a room without windows, that is even better. Use a flashlight or candle to light the room. What does the light do to the darkness? Yes, it chases the light away.

You are like that light here on earth. When you live for God with your whole heart, it is like you reflecting God's light. Others can see Him in you!

SOMETHING ELSE TO DO

Memorize John 8:12a (NKJV).

Jesus spoke to them … saying, "I am the light of the world."

Jesus is the Light of the World

Learn the meaning of the vocabulary word "sin" for the Memory Game.

LESSON 6 Activities

🐦 Draw a circle around the pictures that show someone taking care of God's creation.

🐦 Turn to page 91 of this *Activity Book*. Find Day 2, and color the heavens light blue and the water dark blue.

- Memorize Genesis 1:6 (NKJV).

Then God said, "Let there be a firmament in the midst of the waters, and let it divide the waters from the waters."

- Water a plant inside or outside the house. Watch what happens to the soil and dirt when the plant "drinks" the water.

⊃ Why is it necessary to water the plant?

⊃ How does it "drink" the water?

LESSON 7 Activity

- In the chart below, write down the time you begin this activity.

⊃ Pour water in a small glass. Take a drink, and write down the time.

⊃ Wait a while; then take another drink and write down the time.

⊃ Continue drinking until the glass is empty.

	Time		Time
Take a drink.		**Take a drink.**	
Take a drink.		**Take a drink.**	
Take a drink.		**Take a drink.**	

⊃ Wait a while. Are you getting thirsty?

⊃ You will become thirsty again; but if we love Jesus, our souls are "satisfied" in Him forever.

SOMETHING ELSE TO DO

- Learn John 4:13–14a (NKJV). Memorize the words in **bold**.

Jesus answered and said to her, "Whoever drinks of this water will thirst again, but **whoever drinks of the water that I shall give him will never thirst."**

7

🌿 Learn the meaning of the vocabulary word "soul" for the Memory Game.

Further Study:

🌿 Discuss the following Bible passages that talk about water:

➲ Jesus walks on water: Read Matthew 14:22–33.
(Here are alternate passages: Mark 6:45–51 or John 6:16–21.)

➲ Jesus calms the storm: Read Matthew 8:23–27.
(Here are alternate passages: Mark 4:36–41 or Luke 8:22–25.)

LESSON 8 Activities

🌿 See how difficult it would be to build a town on the water.

➲ *First*, take some Lego® blocks and build a tower or town on the floor.

➲ *Second*, fill up the sink or bathtub with water. Try to build that same tower or town in the water.

➲ Why is land necessary for building a tower or town?

🌿 Turn to page 91 of this *Activity Book*. Find Day 3, and color the land brown.

SOMETHING ELSE TO DO

🌿 Learn Genesis 1:9 (NKJV). Memorize the words in **bold**.

Then God said, "Let the waters under the heavens be gathered together into one place, and **let the dry land appear**"; and it was so.

DAY 3

LESSON 9 Activities

- If weather permits, go outside and collect leaves and flowers. Look at all the different colors, sizes, shapes, and textures.

  - ➲ The word "texture" means how the leaves feel.

  - ➲ Glue the leaves on a piece of construction paper.

- Turn to page 91 of the *Activity Book* and find Day 3. Color the plants green and the water blue.

SOMETHING ELSE TO DO

- Memorize Genesis 1:11 (NKJV). Memorize the words in **bold**.

  Then God said, "Let the earth bring forth grass, the herb that yields seed, and the fruit tree that yields fruit according to its kind, whose seed is in itself, on the earth"; and it was so.

- Plant grass seeds or flowers in a pot. Water the plant and watch it grow over time. If you grow grass, you may even have to trim it!

- Pick a flower and place it in between the pages of a thick book. Use wax paper to protect the paper in the book.

  - ➲ Leave the flower in there for about a week until it is completely dry.

  - ➲ Make a bookmark by gluing the pressed flower onto a piece of construction paper or poster board.

LESSON 10 Activity

- Take a piece of black construction paper and punch holes in it with either scissors or a pencil.

  - ➲ Go into a very dark room, turn out the lights, and hold a flashlight up to the piece of paper. See the "stars" you made.

9

⊃ God made so many stars. Is it possible to count the stars God made? God created the sun, moon, and stars out of nothing just by speaking!

❧ Turn to page 91 of this *Activity Book* and find Day 4. Color the sun and stars yellow and the sky blue.

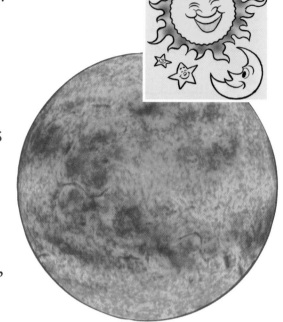

SOMETHING ELSE TO DO

❧ Learn Genesis 1:14a (NKJV). Memorize the words in **bold**.

Then God said, "Let there be lights in the firmament of the heavens to divide the day from the night."

❧ If the weather is warm, go outside on a sunny day and notice how the heat from the sun warms you. If the weather is cold, note how the lack of sun makes the day chilly.

❧ On a clear night, look at the moon and all the stars God made.

LESSON 11 Activities

❧ Make a fish using a paper plate.

⊃ Take the paper plate and flip it bottom-side up on a table. Starting with the outside of the plate, cut out a triangle.

⊃ Flip the plate over and glue the cutout triangle point onto the plate across from where the triangle was originally cut. The cut out triangle is now the fin, and the space where it was cut is the mouth.

⊃ Use sequins, small squares of colored construction paper, or crayons to decorate the fish.

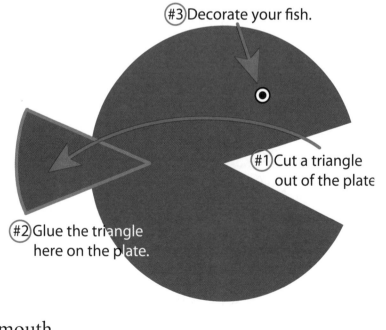

#3 Decorate your fish.

#1 Cut a triangle out of the plate

#2 Glue the triangle here on the plate.

10

❧ Remove this page from the *Activity Book*. Use feathers, narrow strips of construction paper, or some other material to decorate the bird.

❧ Learn Genesis 1:20 (NKJV). Memorize the words in **bold**.

> **Then God said, "Let the waters abound with** an abundance of **living creatures, and let birds fly above the earth** across the face of the firmament of the heavens."

❧ Make a birdfeeder out of an empty 2-liter pop bottle and two quarter-inch dowel rods, each about five inches long.

➲ Wash and rinse the bottle.

➲ Holding the bottle upright, use scissors or sharp knife to cut large holes in all four sides of the bottle for birds to eat.

➲ Cut small holes under the large holes for the dowel rods. Push a rod into a small hole through to the hole on the opposite side of the bottle; do the same with the other rod.

➲ Fill the bottle with birdseed; then tie a piece of string or wire around the lid to hang the birdfeeder on a post or tree branch.

LESSON 12 Activities

❧ Turn to page 91 of this *Activity Book*, and find Day 5. Color the fish and the bird.

❧ Find pictures of birds and fish in magazines, newspapers, or old books. Cut out the pictures and glue them on poster board.

SOMETHING ELSE TO DO

❧ Memorize Genesis 2:15 (NKJV).

Then the LORD God took the man and put him in the garden of Eden to tend and keep it.

❧ If you live close to an aquarium, aviary, or zoo, go on a field trip and look at the beautiful variety of fish and birds that God made. To find an institution near you go on-line to **AmericanZoos.info** for a complete list. Visit **aza.org** (Association of Zoos and Aquariums) for more information.

FURTHER STUDY:

❧ Choose a type of fish or bird that you like very much. Find out where it lives, what it eats, what is unique to that animal, and other interesting facts.

LESSON 13 Activity

❧ Find pictures of land animals by gathering old magazines, newspapers, or books. Cut the pictures out and make a collage on poster board.

SOMETHING ELSE TO DO

❧ Learn Genesis 1:24 (NKJV). Memorize the words in **bold**.

Then God said, "Let the earth bring forth the living creature according to its kind: cattle and creeping thing and beast of the earth, each according to its kind"; and it was so.

FURTHER STUDY:

❧ Choose a type of land animal that you like very much. Find out where it lives, what it eats, what is unique to that animal, and other interesting facts.

LESSON 14 Activities

- ❧ In the textbook, place a star by the animals that make good pets. Put a circle around those animals that give or make something people can eat or use. Animals that should have a star by them are hamster, puppies, and cat. Animals that should have a circle are chicken, cow, and sheep. The horse could be marked either way.

- ❧ Turn to page 91 of this *Activity Book*, and find Day 6. Color only the animals.

SOMETHING ELSE TO DO

- ❧ Learn Genesis 1:25 (NKJV). Memorize the words in **bold**.

  And God made the beast of the earth according to its kind, **cattle** according to its kind, **and everything that creeps on the earth** according to its kind. And God saw that it was good.

LESSON 15 Activities

- ❧ Look in the mirror and discuss what it means to be an image. Make different faces in the mirror.

- ❧ Play "Mirror Me" with someone by facing him or her and making different faces. Your partner must do exactly as you do as if you are looking in the mirror. Take turns being the mirror.

SOMETHING ELSE TO DO

- ❧ Learn Genesis 1:26 (NKJV). Memorize the words in **bold**.

  Then God said, "Let Us make man in Our image, according to Our likeness; let them have dominion over the fish of the sea, over the birds of the air, and over the cattle, over all the earth and over every creeping thing that creeps on the earth."

- ❧ Learn the meaning of the vocabulary word "image" for the Memory Game. By now you should have enough words to play the Memory Game.

LESSON 16 Activities

❧ Think of someone you know very well, or an animal, and imitate that person or animal. Talk how he or she talks, walk how he or she walks, and dress how he or she would dress.

❧ Color the picture below of Adam in the garden naming the animals.

- Turn to page 91 of this *Activity Book*, and find Day 6. Color the picture of the man.

SOMETHING ELSE TO DO

- Memorize Genesis 3:17b (NKJV).

Cursed is the ground for your sake; in toil you shall eat of it all the days of your life.

LESSON 17 Activities

- Review the six days of creation by drawing a line from each day of creation to what was created on that day.

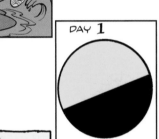

Day 1

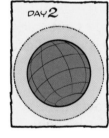

Day 2

Day 3

Day 4

Day 5

Day 6

- Turn to page 91 of this *Activity Book*, and find Day 7. Color the picture. Remove the page from the *Activity Book*, cut along the dotted lines, and attach the pieces of paper together to form a timeline.

SOMETHING ELSE TO DO

- Learn Genesis 2:3 (NKJV). Memorize the words in **bold**.

Then God blessed the seventh day and sanctified it, because in it **He rested from all His work** which God had created and made.

- Learn the meaning of the vocabulary word "heaven." Add the word **heaven** to your Memory Game.

FURTHER STUDY:

Read Genesis 1. What did God say about the creation He had made? (Fill in the blank.)

Genesis 1:10

And God called the dry land Earth, and the gathering
together of the waters He called Seas. And God saw that it was _____.

Genesis 1:12

And the earth brought forth grass, the herb that yields seed
according to its kind, and the tree that yields fruit,
whose seed is in itself according to its kind. And God saw that it was _____.

Genesis 1:18

and to rule over the day and over the night,
and to divide the light from the darkness. And God saw that it was _____.

Genesis 1:21

So God created great sea creatures and every living thing that moves,
with which the waters abounded, according to their kind,
and every winged bird according to its kind. And God saw that it was _____.

Genesis 1:25

And God made the beast of the earth according to its kind,
cattle according to its kind, and everything that creeps
on the earth according to its kind. And God saw that it was _____.

Genesis 1:31

Then God saw everything that He had made, and indeed it was _____

_____.

UNIT 3: *The Little Pilgrim*

LESSON 18 Activity

❧ Match the "privilege" on the left-hand side of the page to the responsibility on the right-hand side. Then color the pictures.

SOMETHING ELSE TO DO

❧ Learn Genesis 1:28 (NKJV). Memorize the words in **bold**.

> And God said to them, "Be fruitful and multiply; fill the earth and subdue it; **have dominion over the fish** of the sea, **over the birds** of the air, **and over every living thing** that moves on the earth."

❧ Make a responsibility chart. On a piece of paper or poster board, list the things you do, including your chores, on the left-hand side of the page. Then make columns for each day of the week. (You may copy the chart on page 40 of this *Activity Book*.) Here is an example:

	Sunday	Monday	Tuesday	Wednes-day	Thursday	Friday	Saturday
Make my bed	★	★	★	★	★	★	★
Brush my teeth	★	★	★	★	★	★	★
Get dressed	★	★	★	★	★	★	★
Devotions with Dad	★	★	★	★	★	★	★
Do my homework		★	★		★	★	
Pick up my toys			★				★
Set/clear the table		★		★		★	

❧ Put a star or sticker next to each thing you do.

LESSON 19 Activity

❧ Create a new creature and draw it on the next page. Then color it. Decide what it eats, where it lives, and what it likes to do. Then give it a name.

My creature's name is _____ .

It eats _____ .

It lives _____ .

It likes to _____ .

My creature is really _____ .

❧ God gave Adam and Eve the special job of naming all of the creatures in the garden.

20

Draw your creature here:

SOMETHING ELSE TO DO

- Memorize Genesis 2:18 (NKJV).

    And the LORD God said, "It is not good that man should be alone; I will make him a helper."

- Learn the meaning of the vocabulary word "cultivate." Add the word **cultivate** to your Memory Game.

LESSON 20 Activity

Activity:

🖎 Put the events in order. Write a number "1" in the box provided for the event that happened first, a number "2" for what happened second, and so forth.

SOMETHING ELSE TO DO

- Learn Genesis 2:16–17 (NKJV). Memorize the words in **bold**.

  And the LORD God commanded the man, saying, "Of every tree of the garden you may freely eat; but **of the tree of the knowledge of good and evil you shall not eat,** for in the day that you eat of it you shall surely die."

- Learn the meaning of the vocabulary word "tempted." Add the word **tempted** to your Memory Game.

FURTHER STUDY:

- Read Genesis 3:1–6.

Now the serpent was more cunning than any beast of the field which the LORD God had made. And he said to the woman, "Has God indeed said, 'You shall not eat of every tree of the garden'?"

And the woman said to the serpent, "We may eat the fruit of the trees of the garden; but of the fruit of the tree which is in the midst of the garden, God has said, 'You shall not eat it, nor shall you touch it, lest you die.'"

Then the serpent said to the woman, "You will not surely die. For God knows that in the day you eat of it your eyes will be opened, and you will be like God, knowing good and evil."

So when the woman saw that the tree was good for food, that it was pleasant to the eyes, and a tree desirable to make one wise, she took of its fruit and ate. She also gave to her husband with her, and he ate.

- ⊃ What would you have done if you were in Adam and Eve's place?

- ⊃ What should Adam and Eve have done?

- ⊃ When were you tempted?

- ⊃ Were you ever tempted to break a rule?

Pray that God would help you to obey and not give in to the temptation.

LESSON 21 Activity

❧ Color the pictures of what happens to the piggy bank.

SOMETHING ELSE TO DO

❧ Learn Matthew 26:41 (NKJV). Memorize the words in **bold**.

Watch and pray, lest you enter into temptation.
The spirit indeed is willing, but the flesh is weak.

LESSON 22 Activity

☙ What is happening in each picture? Put an "X" through the pictures that illustrate sinful behavior. Color the pictures that are showing godly behavior.

🕊 Learn Genesis 3:6 (NKJV). Memorize the words in **bold**.

When the woman saw that the tree was good for food, that it was pleasant to the eyes, and a tree desirable to make one wise, **she took of its fruit and ate. She also gave to her husband with her, and he ate.**

LESSON 23 Activity

🕊 Color the picture of the tree in the garden with the serpent.

↻ Should Adam and Eve have taken the fruit and eaten it?

↻ What should they have said to the snake?

🍃 Memorize 1 Corinthians 15:22a (NKJV).

For as in Adam all die.

LESSON 24 Activity

🍃 Color the picture of Adam and Eve hiding behind the bush. Remove this page and cut out the picture. Carefully cut on the line at the bottom of the picture.

✂ Cut on line.

🍃 Make a diorama using an old shoebox. Fold the tabs and glue them down towards the front of the box. Decorate the box to look like a garden.

SOMETHING ELSE TO DO

🍃 Learn Genesis 3:11b–12 (NKJV). Memorize the words in **bold**.

And [God] said, "… Have you eaten from the tree of which I commanded you that you should not eat?" Then the man said, "The woman whom You gave to be with me, she gave me of the tree, and I ate."

LESSON 25 Activities

✌ Color the image of the cross crushing the serpent.

✌ Read Genesis 3:15. The crown represents King Jesus; He died on the cross not only to pay for our sins but also to destroy Satan. Who is Satan in the picture?

❧ Listen as your teacher reads each of the following sentences. Write "T" if it is true or "F" if it is false.

_____ Adam and Eve ate the fruit.

_____ Adam and Eve were happy when they realized they disobeyed God.

_____ God knew right away that they had disobeyed Him.

_____ God gave them a chance to tell the truth.

_____ Adam and Eve told God they were sorry.

_____ God showed Adam and Eve grace and did not give them the punishment they deserved.

SOMETHING ELSE TO DO

❧ Memorize Genesis 3:15 (NKJV).

[God said to Satan], "And I will put enmity between you and the woman, and between your seed and her Seed; **He shall bruise your head, and you shall bruise His heel."**

❧ Learn the meaning of the vocabulary word "grace." Add the word **grace** to your Memory Game.

LESSON 26 Activity

❧ Look at the pictures on the next page. Draw a line to match what each child needs to do to fix what he or she has done. Then color the pictures.

⊃ Spilling milk ➡ cleaning it up

⊃ Coloring on the wall ➡ washing it off

⊃ Messy room ➡ clean it up

SOMETHING ELSE TO DO

❧ Memorize Genesis 3:21 (NKJV).

Also for Adam and his wife the LORD God made tunics of skin, and clothed them.

LESSON 27 Activity

❧ Find old fabric, felt, or construction paper. Cut out clothes to fit Adam and Eve; then glue the clothes on Adam and Eve. If you do not have material, you may color their clothes. Color the rest of the picture.

❧ Memorize John 3:16 (NKJV).

For God so loved the world that He gave His only begotten Son, that whoever believes in Him should not perish, but have everlasting life.

❧ Learn the meaning of the vocabulary word "substitute." Add the word **substitute** to your Memory Game.

LESSON 28 Activities

❧ Stand on your bed or something high. Now jump in my arms. Did you trust that I would catch you?

❧ This is an example of trust—I said I would catch you and I did. We can trust God will take us to heaven someday.

❧ Color the picture of David and Goliath.

❧ David put his trust in God alone—even in the face of a great enemy.

SOMETHING ELSE TO DO

- Learn Romans 6:1–2 (NKJV). Memorize the words in **bold**.

  What shall we say then? Shall we continue in sin that grace may abound? Certainly not! How shall we who died to sin live any longer in it?

- Learn the meaning of the vocabulary word "trust." Add the word **trust** to your Memory Game.

FURTHER STUDY:

- Read Genesis 3:1–19.

  ⊃ What did God promise Adam and Eve?

  ⊃ What did they do to deserve God's grace?

  ⊃ Why did God show them grace?

UNIT 4: *The Little Pilgrim's Family*

LESSON 29 Activities

- On blank paper, draw a picture of a family member or glue his or her photo. How much do you love this person? What do you love about this person?

- Color the picture of Cain and Abel.

SOMETHING ELSE TO DO

- Memorize Mark 3:35 (NKJV).

For whoever does the will of God is My brother and My sister and mother.

LESSON 30 Activity

❧ What are the children doing in each of these pictures? Put an "X" on the pictures that show someone being selfish.

SOMETHING ELSE TO DO

- Learn Matthew 22:37–40 (NKJV). Memorize the words in **bold**.

  Jesus said to him, "'**You shall love the LORD your God with all your heart, with all your soul, and with all your mind**.' This is the first and great commandment. And the second is like it: '**You shall love your neighbor as yourself**.' On these two commandments hang all the Law and the Prophets."

- Learn the meaning of the vocabulary word "selfish." Add the word **selfish** to your Memory Game.

- Think of different ways you can serve someone in your family. Choose one way to serve, and then serve one family member this week.

FURTHER STUDY:

- Read Luke 10:30–37. This story is called the parable of the Good Samaritan.

  - What happened to the man who went down from Jerusalem to Jericho?

  - Who came by first? What did he do to help the man?

  - Who came by second? What did he do to help the man?

  - Who came by third? What did he do to help the man?

  - What did the Good Samaritan do the next day when he had to leave?

  - Which one was a neighbor to the man who fell among the thieves?

  - How does this parable help us understand Mark 12:33?

- As time permits, you may choose to go over other examples in the Bible of people who served others.

  - Joseph serves Potiphar (Genesis 39:1–6)

  - Ruth serves her mother-in-law, Naomi (Ruth 1:15–18; 2:11, 12)

  - Jesus serves the disciples by washing their feet (John 13:1–5)

  - The early church in Acts (Acts 2:42–47)

LESSON 31 Activities

❧ Look at some ice cubes; do they feel cold? See what comes from the teakettle; what is it called? (*steam*) Then turn on the water from the faucet. All three of these are water, but they have different forms—solid, gas, and liquid.

❧ In the same way, God shows Himself to us as the Father, the Son, and the Holy Spirit. He is called the Trinity—one God, but three Persons.

❧ Fill in the other two Persons of the Trinity. (*Answers*: **Holy Spirit**, **Son**)

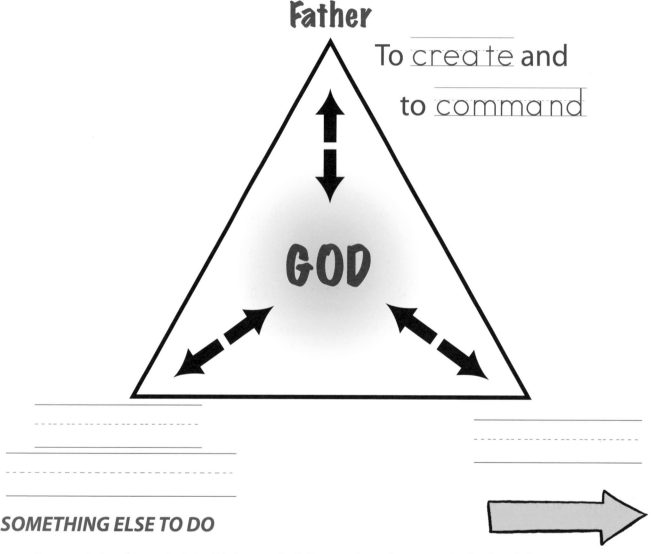

Father

To create and

to command

GOD

SOMETHING ELSE TO DO

❧ Learn Matthew 3:16–17 (NKJV). Memorize the words in **bold**.

When He had been baptized, Jesus came up immediately from the water; and behold, the heavens were opened to Him, and **He saw the Spirit of God descending** like a dove and alighting **upon Him. And** suddenly **a voice came from heaven, saying, "This is My beloved Son, in whom I am well pleased."**

- Read *3 in 1: A Picture of God* by Joanne Marxhausen. Use an apple as you read the book to help illustrate the Trinity.

LESSON 32 Activity

- Fill in the jobs of Jesus, the Son of God, on the Trinity triangle. (*Answers*: **live**, **die**)

Father

To <u>create</u> and to <u>command</u>

GOD

Holy Spirit

Son

To _____ perfectly and to _____ on the cross for our sins

SOMETHING ELSE TO DO

- Memorize John 14:26 (NKJV).

But the Helper, the Holy Spirit, whom the Father will send in My name, He will teach you all things, and bring to your remembrance all things that I said to you.

🕊 Name some things and chores you have to do. Fill out the job chart. You may copy the chart below or make your own.

	Sunday	Monday	Tuesday	Wednesday	Thursday	Friday	Saturday
Make my bed							
Brush my teeth							
Get dressed							
Devotions with Dad							
Do my homework							
Pick up my toys							
Set & clear the table							

↪ Put a star or sticker in the correct square once you complete each job or responsibility. Be sure to put it under the right day of the week.

LESSON 33 Activities

❧ Color the picture of Adam and Eve in the heart.

❧ Interview your mom and dad (or grandparents or a married couple that you know) about their marriage.

A few easy ways to record the answers are by using a video phone, digital camcorder, or some kind of recording device.

Here are some questions to ask,
but you may make up your own.

➲ How long have you been married?

➲ What do you love most about being married?

➲ What is the hardest thing about being married?

➲ What have you learned since being married?

SOMETHING ELSE TO DO

☙ Learn Ephesians 5:33 (NKJV). Memorize the words in **bold**.

Let each one of you in particular **so love his own wife as himself, and let the wife see that she respects her husband.**

LESSON 34 Activity

☙ Your teacher will read each of the following sentences to you. Then you write an "H" if the sentence is true for a husband or "W" if it is true for his wife.

____Love your wife as yourself.

____Honor and obey your husband.

____You are to serve and take care of your wife.

____You should be willing to lay down your life for your wife.

____You are to help your husband.

SOMETHING ELSE TO DO

☙ Learn Ephesians 5:25–27 (NKJV). Memorize the words in **bold**.

Husbands, love your wives, just as Christ also loved the church and gave Himself for her, that He might sanctify and cleanse her with the washing of water by the word, that He might present her to Himself a glorious church, not having spot or wrinkle or any such thing, but that she should be holy and without blemish.

ঌ Learn the meaning of the vocabulary word "bride." Add the word **bride** to your Memory Game.

FURTHER STUDY:

ঌ Read Ephesians 5:28–33. This is what the Bible teaches about marriage.

- ⊃ How should a husband love his wife? (verses 28–29)

- ⊃ What should a man do when he gets married? (verse 31)

- ⊃ What is the great mystery that Paul is speaking about? (verse 32)

- ⊃ How should a husband love his wife? (verse 33a)

- ⊃ How should a wife love her husband? (verse 33b)

ঌ If time permits, study Colossians 3:18–19; 1 Peter 3:1, 7.

LESSON 35 Activities

❧ Parents are to love their children more than themselves. How do your parents show their love to you? Think of ways to thank them for the love that they give to you. You can make a card, draw a picture, or make a gift for them.

❧ Color the picture of the child and his parents **reconciled** (*brought back together in love and forgiveness*). When have your parents forgiven you?

SOMETHING ELSE TO DO

❧ Memorize Ephesians 6:4 (NKJV).

Fathers, do not provoke your children to wrath, but bring them up in the training and admonition of the Lord.

❧ Learn the meaning of the vocabulary word "discipline." Add the word **discipline** to your Memory Game.

LESSON 36 Activity

❧ How have your parents obeyed God's command to "be fruitful and multiply"? Make a collage using family photographs or by drawing pictures of yourself and your siblings.

SOMETHING ELSE TO DO

❧ Memorize Hebrews 12:6 (NKJV).

For whom the Lord loves He chastens, and scourges every son whom He receives.

FURTHER STUDY:

❧ **Rules of the Home:**

➲ What are some of the rules your parents have in the house?

➲ How do these rules show that your parents love you?

> ### Be Fruitful and Multiply
>
> . So God created man in His own image; in the image of God He created him; male and female He created them.
>
> Then God blessed them, and God said to them, "Be fruitful and multiply; fill the earth and subdue it; have dominion over the fish of the sea, over the birds of the air, and over every living thing that moves on the earth."
>
> *Genesis 1:27–28*

> ### Be Kind and Tender-Hearted
>
> And be ye kind one to another, tenderhearted, forgiving one another, even as God for Christ's sake hath forgiven you.
>
> *Ephesians 4:32*

LESSON 37 Activity

🙩 Color the picture of the little children giving their hearts to Jesus.

SOMETHING ELSE TO DO

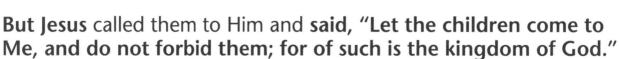

🙩 Memorize Luke 18:16 (NKJV).

But Jesus called them to Him and **said,** "Let the children come to Me, and do not forbid them; for of such is the kingdom of God."

46

LESSON 38 Activities

❧ God has given us wonderful promises that we know that He will keep. Let us read John 14:2–3, and you write down the promise Jesus made.

❧ Draw a picture of what you think heaven looks like.

❧ Let us read 1 Corinthians 10:13. How does God help us when we are tempted? (cf. Romans 5:12–14)

SOMETHING ELSE TO DO

&❧ Memorize Deuteronomy 31:6 (NKJV).

Be strong and of good courage, do not fear nor be afraid of them; for the LORD your God, He is the One who goes with you. He will not leave you nor forsake you.

FURTHER STUDY:

&❧ Read Luke 18:15–17.

   ➲ Whom did the people bring to Jesus? (verse 15a)

   ➲ What did the disciples do to the people? (verse 15b)

   ➲ But what did Jesus say to His disciples? (verse 16)

   ➲ How should we receive the kingdom of God? (verse 17)

LESSON 39 Activities

&❧ Remove the next page from this *Activity Book*, cut out the verse, and color the word "honor." Glue the verse onto cardboard or poster board and hang it in your room. Pray that God will help you to honor and obey your parents.

&❧ Cut out the "cross bookmark" on the next page. Glue the cross to cardboard or poster board. Next, color and decorate it; then give the cross bookmark to your parents or someone else you love.

SOMETHING ELSE TO DO

&❧ Memorize Exodus 20:12 (NKJV).

Honor your father and your mother, that your days may be long upon the land which the LORD your God is giving you.

&❧ Learn the meaning of the vocabulary word "honor." Add the word **honor** to your Memory Game.

HONOR

Honor your father and your mother, that your days may be long upon the land which the LORD your God is giving you.

Exodus 20:12

• Cut out the Bible verse above.
• Cut along the dotted line.
• Color the word "HONOR" blue.
• Glue it to a piece of poster board.
• Hang it in your room.

• Cut out the bookmark at the right.
• Cut along the dotted line.
• Color and decorate the cross.
• Give it to someone you love.

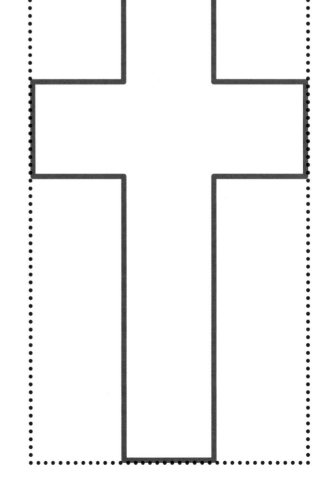

LESSON 40 Activities

- Color the word "serve" red.

- How can you serve your brother? Your sister? Your mom? Your dad? Your neighbor? Your friend?

- Color the picture of Christ's death on the cross.

- How did Christ serve His special people by dying and rising from the dead? (Romans 5:8–11)

SOMETHING ELSE TO DO

- Memorize 3 John 1:4 (NKJV).

I have no greater joy than to hear that my children walk in truth.

- Think of ways you can serve others. Do it right away!

UNIT 5: The Little Pilgrim and Church

LESSON 41 Activities

- Color the pictures for the "Faith Booklet" on the next page. Cut out each man and woman of faith. Then staple them together to make a booklet.

- Read the following passages. How do these people of faith reflect God's light? Can you guess which story goes with each picture in your "Faith Booklet"?

  ⊃ Noah (Genesis 6–9:17)

  ⊃ Sarah (Genesis 21:1–7)

  ⊃ Abraham and Isaac (Genesis 22:1–18)

  ⊃ Isaac and Rebekah (Genesis 24:61–67)

SOMETHING ELSE TO DO

- Learn Hebrews 11:1–2 (NKJV). Memorize the words in **bold**.

Now faith is the substance of things hoped for, the evidence of things not seen. For by it the elders obtained a good testimony.

- Learn the meaning of the vocabulary word "faith." Add the word **faith** to your Memory Game.

LESSON 42 Activities

☙ Color the map of Israel.

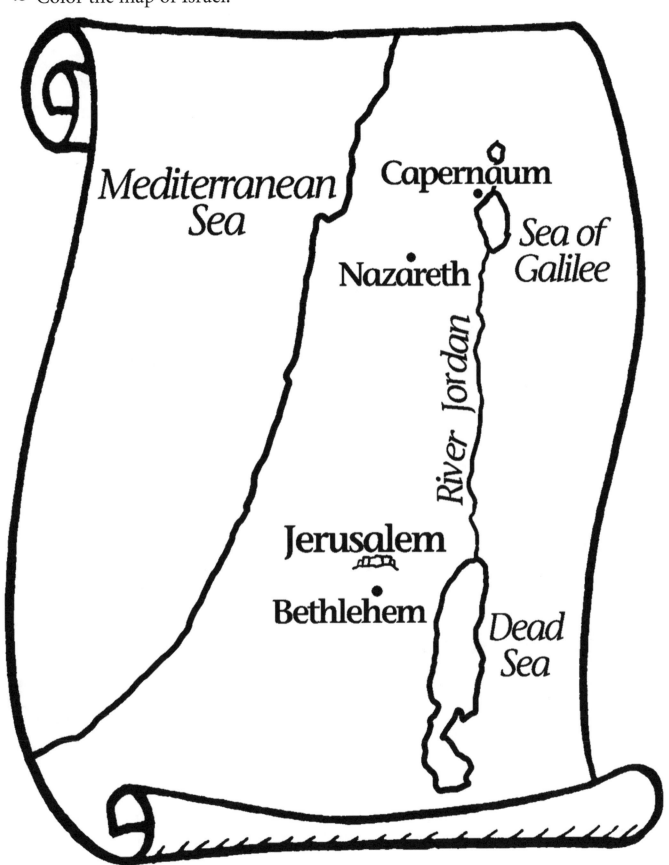

᠁ Read Hebrews 11:1–11. (*If time permits, you can read the whole of the chapter.*)

➲ What did Abel receive from God for his faith? (verse 4)

➲ Who pleased God so much that he did not see death? (verse 5)

➲ By faith what did Noah do? (verse 7)

➲ Who left his home by faith and move to the place of his inheritance? (verse 8) Who shared in that inheritance? (verse 9)

➲ By faith Sarah was able to do what in her old age? (verse 11)

As time permits, you may ask the following questions now or at a another time.

➲ How did God test Abraham's faith? (verse 17)

➲ What did Isaac do by faith for his sons? (verse 20)

➲ What did Jacob do by faith when he was dying? (verse 21)

➲ What other men and women are mentioned in this chapter for their faith?

SOMETHING ELSE TO DO

᠁ Learn Hebrews 11:13 (NKJV). Memorize the words in **bold**.

These all died in faith, not having received the promises, but having seen them afar off were assured of them, embraced them **and confessed that they were strangers and pilgrims on the earth.**

LESSON 43 Activities

᠁ Use an empty paper towel roll or rolled up construction paper. Make a megaphone for proclaiming the good news of Jesus. Decorate it with stickers, markers, crayons, and so forth.

᠁ Tell your friend or cousin about Jesus.
You can invite that person to Sunday school or children's club to hear more about how Christ died for the sins of His special people.

SOMETHING ELSE TO DO

🕊 Learn Matthew 28:18–20 (NKJV). Memorize the words in **bold**.

And Jesus came and spoke to them, saying, "All authority has been given to Me in heaven and on earth. **Go therefore and make disciples of all the nations**, baptizing them in the name of the Father and of the Son and of the Holy Spirit, teaching them to observe all things that I have commanded you; **and lo, I am with you always, even to the end of the age**.

LESSON 44 Activities

🕊 Include the jobs of the Holy Spirit in the "Trinity triangle."
(*Answers*: **guide**, **protect**)

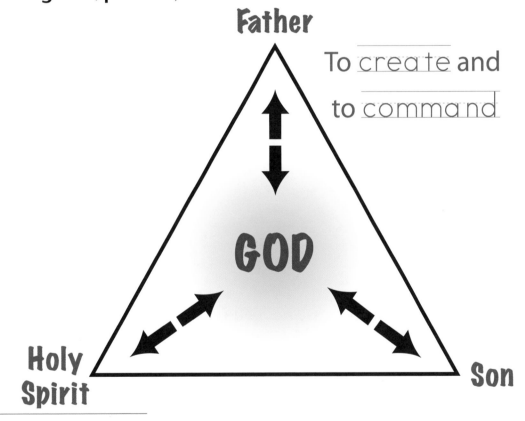

Father

To <u>create</u> and

to <u>command</u>

GOD

Holy
Spirit

Son

To _____ and

to _____

God's special people

To <u>live</u> perfectly

and to <u>die</u> on the

cross for our sins

✺ Color the picture of Polycarp being burned at the stake.

✺ He was called a **martyr** because he died because of his belief in God. Would you be willing to die for Jesus like Polycarp did?

SOMETHING ELSE TO DO

✺ Learn Acts 2:38 (NKJV). Memorize the words in **bold**.

Then Peter said to them, **"Repent, and let every one of you be baptized in the name of Jesus Christ for the remission of sins; and you shall receive the gift of the Holy Spirit. …"**

✺ Learn the meaning of the vocabulary word "martyr."
Add the word **martyr** to your Memory Game.

🕊 Look up and read about some of the men of faith listed in this lesson.

    ✝ Polycarp   ✿ Martin Luther   ✍ John Calvin

LESSON 45 Activity

🕊 Color the six pictures on page 61. Cut them out and then glue them onto paper or poster board to make a banner or scroll that proclaims the good news of the gospel. Here is an example of what it will look like:

1. Christ died on the cross.
2. Christ rose from the dead.
3. Jesus is in heaven with God.

4. God takes away our sins.
5. God loves us.
6. Jesus will come back someday.

SOMETHING ELSE TO DO

🕊 Learn Acts 28:30–31 (ɴᴋᴊᴠ). Memorize the words in **bold**.

Then Paul dwelt two whole years in his own rented house, and **received all who came to him, preaching the kingdom of God** and teaching the things which concern the Lord Jesus Christ with all confidence, no one forbidding him.

FURTHER STUDY:

🕊 Read about how God changed Paul's heart in Acts 9:1–19.

➲ How did God speak to Saul on the road to Damacus? (verse 3)

➲ What did Jesus say to Paul? (verses 4–6)

➲ What did Jesus tell Ananias to do for Paul? (verses 11-15)

➲ How did Ananias help Saul? (verses 17–18)

➲ What did Saul do after meeting with Ananias? (verses 18–20)

LESSON 46 Activity

☙ Match the part of the human body that best represents the part of the body of Christ. Write your answers on the correct lines next to the picture of the man preaching below.

↻ **mouth**—pastor to preach the Word

↻ **head**—elders to make decisions and think through problems

↻ **hands**—deacons who help others

↻ **ears**—congregation as they listen to God's Word

↻ **feet**—church that runs to proclaim the good news of the gospel

SOMETHING ELSE TO DO

🕊 Learn 1 Corinthians 12:12 (NKJV). Memorize the words in **bold**.

For as the body is one and has many members, but all the members of that one body, being many, are one body, **so also is Christ.**

FURTHER STUDY:

🕊 Set up an interview with your **pastor**, **elder**, or **deacon** at your church. You may use the questions below, or you may come up with some of your own. Ask someone to write down the answers for you, or use a recording device for the interview.

➲ How long have you been a pastor? (or an elder? or a deacon?)

➲ What made you want to be a pastor? (or an elder? or a deacon?)

➲ What are some things you do as a pastor? (or an elder? or a deacon?)

➲ What is the hardest part of your job?

➲ How can the congregation pray for you as you do your job?

LESSON 47 Activity

🕊 Using a bulletin from a previous Sunday service, go over the different parts of worship. Underline the parts, such as *singing*, *reading the Bible*, and *praying*.

SOMETHING ELSE TO DO

🕊 Learn Exodus 20:8–10a (NKJV). Memorize the words in **bold**.

Remember the Sabbath day, to keep it holy. Six days you shall labor and do all your work, but the seventh day is the Sabbath of the LORD your God.

LESSON 48 Activity

❧ Heaven is going to be wonderful. Draw a picture of what you are looking forward to doing or seeing when in heaven.

SOMETHING ELSE TO DO

❧ Learn Exodus 20:11 (NKJV). Memorize the words in **bold**.

For in six days the LORD made the heavens and the earth, the sea, and all that is in them, and rested the seventh day. Therefore **the LORD blessed the Sabbath day and hallowed it.**

LESSON 49 Activities

❧ Color the picture of the children going to church.

ea Here are some questions about being active in church:

⊃ What kind of activities do you do in the church?

⊃ What kind of activities do you do at home?

⊃ What kind of activities do you do in the community?

ea Serving is a wonderful way to show our love for God and His people. Can you think of ways you could serve the following people?

⊃ When Mom is making dinner …

⊃ When little sister cannot reach something …

⊃ When the neighbor's mailman drops off mail …

⊃ When a church member in a wheelchair takes off coat …

⊃ When an elderly person is sad …

SOMETHING ELSE TO DO

ea Learn Psalm 150:3–6 (NKJV). Memorize the words in **bold**.

Praise Him with the sound of the trumpet; praise Him with the lute and harp! Praise Him with the timbrel and dance; praise Him with stringed instruments and flutes! Praise Him with loud cymbals; praise Him with clashing cymbals! **Let everything that has breath praise the LORD. Praise the LORD!**

UNIT 6: *The Little Pilgrim and Society*

LESSON 50 Activities

🐦 Color the picture of the bully acting badly.

🐦 How do you think Jesus wants to respond?

☙ Read Ephesians 4:32.

➲ How can you be kind to your sisters? brothers? cousins? friends? neighbors?

➲ What does it mean to be tender-hearted?

➲ How can you forgive others like Christ forgave you?

SOMETHING ELSE TO DO

☙ Learn Matthew 5:43–45a (NKJV). Memorize the words in **bold**.

You have heard that it was said, "You shall love your neighbor and hate your enemy." **But I say to you, love your enemies … and pray for those who … persecute you**, that you may be sons of your Father in heaven.

☙ Learn the meaning of the vocabulary word "mercy." Add the word **mercy** to your Memory Game.

FURTHER STUDY:

☙ Read Matthew 5:43–48.

➲ What does "persecute" mean?

➲ Why is it hard to love those who persecute you?

➲ How is it possible to love them?

Polycarp was a faithful pastor who preached the good news about Jesus Christ. But the people of his hometown Smyrna did not like his preaching. So they burned Polycarp on a pile of wood. He became a martyr because he believed that Jesus is Lord. Polycarp died for his faith.

LESSON 51 Activity

- Color the picture.

- How does the babysitter protect the child?

- What other people protect you besides your parents? (**Possible answers:** grandparents, pastors, teachers, police, firemen, doctors, dentists, and many more).

Learn Romans 13:1 (NKJV). Memorize the words in **bold**.

Let every soul be subject to the governing authorities. **For there is no authority except from God, and the authorities that exist are appointed by God.**

LESSON 52 Activity

Pretend you are in charge of the playground. It is like being the head of the government. Look at these pictures. What "good rules" would you make?

- Learn Romans 13:3–4 (NKJV). Memorize the words in **bold**.

  For rulers are not a terror to good works, but to evil. Do you want to be unafraid of the authority? Do what is good, and you will have praise from the same. For he is God's minister to you for good. But if you do evil, be afraid; for he does not bear the sword in vain; for he is God's minister, an avenger to execute wrath on him who practices evil.

- Learn the meaning of the vocabulary word "government." Add the word **government** to your Memory Game.

FURTHER STUDY:

- Go to your library and check out books to learn more about your government.

LESSON 53 Activities

- Ask your parents about their rules. How are these rules intended to protect and keep you safe?

- God's special people can change bad laws that harm people in the following ways:

  ➲ **We can vote** for people, who love God and His Word, to represent us in government and to get rid of the bad laws;

  ➲ **We can warn people** from God's Word and help them to obey Him;

  ➲ **We can pray** for those who rule over us (1 Timothy 2:1–4) and for our country to turn from its wicked ways (2 Chronicles 7:14); and

  ➲ **We can trust God** to care for us (Ezekiel 34:15, 16).

> Our government is based on God's rules found in the Bible. These rules are called the Law of God. What part of God's Law does the picture above represent? (**Answer:** *the Ten Commandments*)

SOMETHING ELSE TO DO

🕊 Learn Jeremiah 29:4–5, 7 (NKJV). Memorize the words in **bold**.

Thus says the LORD of Hosts, the God of Israel, to all who were carried away captive, whom I have caused to be carried away from Jerusalem to Babylon: Build houses and dwell in them; plant gardens and eat their fruit. … And **seek the peace of the city where I have caused you to be carried away captive, and pray to the LORD for it; for in its peace you will have peace.**

LESSON 54 Activity

🕊 On the next page, cut out God's **Ten Commandments**. Put them in order, and glue them on a separate piece of paper or poster board.

SOMETHING ELSE TO DO

🕊 Learn John 14:2–3 (NKJV). Memorize the words in **bold**.

In My Father's house are many mansions; if it were not so, I would have told you. I go to prepare a place for you. And if I go and prepare a place for you, I will come again and receive you to Myself; that where I am, there you may be also.

FURTHER STUDY:

🕊 Read about God's **Ten Commandments** in Exodus 20.

➲ Which rules tell how we should worship God? (*commandments 1–4*)

➲ Which rules tell us how to treat others? (*commandments 6–10*)

➲ Can we worship other gods? graven images? (*No, we worship God alone.*)

➲ How should we remember the Sabbath?

➲ How does each of God's rules keep you and others safe?

7　You shall not commit adultery.

- -

10　You shall not covet your neighbor's house; you shall not covet your neighbor's wife, nor his male servant, nor his female servant, nor his ox, nor his donkey, nor anything that is your neighbor's.

- -

3　You shall not take the name of the LORD your God in vain, for the LORD will not hold him guiltless who takes His name in vain.

- -

5　Honor your father and your mother, that your days may be long upon the land which the LORD your God is giving you.

- -

1　You shall have no other gods before Me.

- -

8　You shall not steal.

- -

2　You shall not make for yourself a carved image—any likeness of anything that is in heaven above, or that is in the earth beneath, or that is in the water under the earth; you shall not bow down to them nor serve them. For I, the LORD your God, am a jealous God, visiting the iniquity of the fathers upon the children to the third and fourth generations of those who hate Me, but showing mercy to thousands, to those who love Me and keep My commandments.

- -

9　You shall not bear false witness against your neighbor.

- -

6　You shall not murder.

- -

4　Remember the Sabbath day, to keep it holy. Six days you shall labor and do all your work, but the seventh day is the Sabbath of the LORD your God. In it you shall do no work: you, nor your son, nor your daughter, nor your male servant, nor your female servant, nor your cattle, nor your stranger who is within your gates. For in six days the LORD made the heavens and the earth, the sea, and all that is in them, and rested the seventh day. Therefore the LORD blessed the Sabbath day and hallowed it.

LESSON 55 Activity

❧ For this activity you will need old magazines, newspapers, or books that may be cut up. Glue and poster board will also be needed for this activity.

➲ Look for different kinds of people from all over the world.

➲ Cut out the pictures of people. You may cut out pictures of people doing different things to show them singing, running, dancing, and so forth.

➲ Make a collage by gluing them on a piece of paper.

SOMETHING ELSE TO DO

❧ Memorize Matthew 5:9 (NKJV).

Blessed are the peacemakers, for they shall be called sons of God.

LESSON 56 Activity

❧ Do you live in a big city or a small town or out in the country? Think about how the following people serve your community.

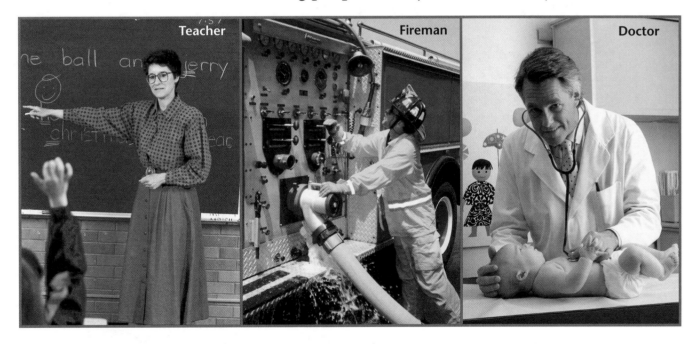

Teacher   Fireman   Doctor

➲ How does a teacher help in your community?

➲ How does a fireman protect you and keep you safe?

➲ How does a doctor help you to stay healthy?

SOMETHING ELSE TO DO

❧ Memorize Matthew 22:39b (NKJV).

You shall love your neighbor as yourself.

❧ Keep your eyes opened for ways others serve you.

    ↪ Be sure to thank them.

    ↪ Think of ways you can serve others.

UNIT 7: *The Little Pilgrim in the World*

LESSON 57 Activities

🍂 Color the picture of the man telling the people about God's Word.

🍂 Talk about how we can make disciples of all nations (Matthew 28:19).

➲ Pray for missionaries that you know and the work God gave them to do.

➲ Encourage them by sending a card or gift to them.

🕊 Memorize Matthew 28:19 (NKJV).

Go therefore and make disciples of all the nations, baptizing them in the name of the Father and of the Son and of the Holy Spirit.

🕊 Learn the meaning of the vocabulary word "apostle." Add the word **apostle** to your Memory Game.

LESSON 58 Activity

🕊 If you have a globe, atlas, or computer, locate the following five countries: the United States, Egypt, China, Brazil, and the United Kingdom. (See also pages 114 and 115 of this *Activity Book*.) Each country is on a different continent, is a different size and shape, and has its own history.

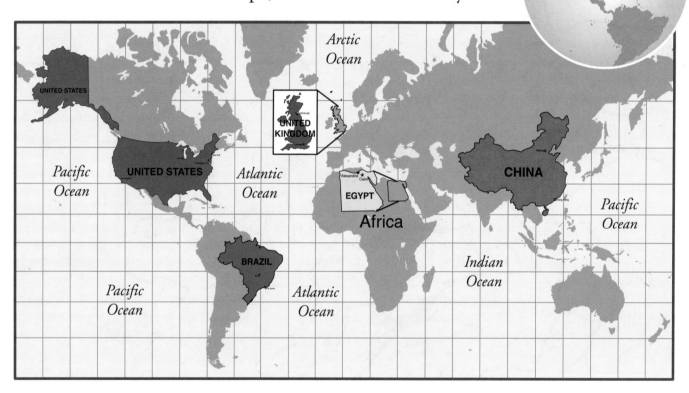

SOMETHING ELSE TO DO

🕊 Learn Revelation 22:17 (NKJV). Memorize the words in **bold**.

And the Spirit and the bride say, "Come!" And let him who hears say, "Come!" **And let him who thirsts come. Whoever desires, let him take the water of life freely.**

🙣 Learn the meaning of the vocabulary word "continent." Add the word **continent** to your Memory Game.

🙣 How many continents are there? (seven)

⮑ Can you name all the continents? (Africa, Antarctica, Asia, Australia, Europe, North America, South America)

⮑ On which continent is each of the five countries mentioned on page 78?

LESSON 59 Activities

🙣 Using the picture of the American flag in the textbook as a guide, color the American flag below.

🙣 Discuss, "How can too much of something be bad?"

SOMETHING ELSE TO DO

🙣 Memorize Matthew 19:24 (NKJV).

And again I say to you, it is easier for a camel to go through the eye of a needle than for a rich man to enter the kingdom of God.

🙣 Learn the meaning of the vocabulary word "freedom." Add the word **freedom** to your Memory Game.

LESSON 60 Activities

❧ Match each word to the correct picture.

vote

worship

speech

serve

❧ Go to pages 114 and 115 of this *Activity Book*, and find the map of the world. Locate the correct outline of the United States, and color it blue.

❧ Color in the word "Jesus" next to the United States map on page 114.

SOMETHING ELSE TO DO

❧ Learn Matthew 6:19–20 (NKJV). Memorize the words in **bold**.

Do not lay up for yourselves treasures on earth, where moth and rust destroy and where thieves break in and steal; but **lay up for yourselves treasures in heaven, where neither moth nor rust destroys and where thieves do not break in and steal.**

FURTHER STUDY:

❧ Find out what other freedoms Americans enjoy.

↪ The first ten amendments to the Constitution, or the Bill of Rights, set forth the priceless rights or freedoms that all Americans may enjoy.

LESSON 61 Activity

☙ Color the Egyptian flag using the picture in the textbook as a guide.

SOMETHING ELSE TO DO

☙ Memorize Hosea 11:1 (NKJV).

When Israel was a child, I loved him, and out of Egypt I called My son.

يَسُوع
Jesus

LESSON 62 Activities

☙ Go to pages 114 and 115 of this *Activity Book*, and find the map of the world. Locate the correct outline of Egypt, and color it yellow.

☙ Study the Egyptian word (يَسُوع) for the name of "Jesus." On the world map on page 114, color it yellow. Although we speak different languages and our alphabets may be different, we are all one in Jesus.

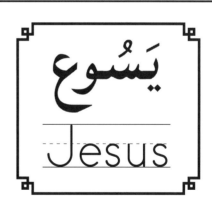

SOMETHING ELSE TO DO

&. Memorize Exodus 20:3 (NKJV).

You shall have no other gods before Me.

FURTHER STUDY:

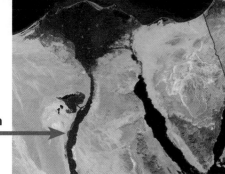

Nile River as seen from Space ⟶

&. Research the Nile River.

⊃ Where does the Nile River begin? (*Lake Victoria, Uganda*)

⊃ What are the two main rivers that flow into the Nile? (*Blue & White Nile*)

⊃ What did the Aswan High Dam stop on the Nile River? (*flooding*)

⊃ Why is the Nile River so important to the people of Egypt? (*fishing, shipping, watering crops, drinking water, boating, generating electricity*)

LESSON 63 Activity

&. Color the Chinese flag using the picture in the textbook as a guide.

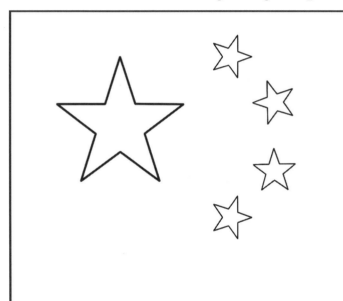

SOMETHING ELSE TO DO

❧ Memorize John 15:20 (NKJV).

Remember the word that I said to you, "A servant is not greater than his master." If they persecuted Me, they will also persecute you.

LESSON 64 Activity

❧ Go to page 115 of this *Activity Book* and find the map of the world. Locate the correct outline of China, and color it red.

❧ Using a thin paintbrush, copy the Chinese word for Jesus found here:

耶穌

SOMETHING ELSE TO DO

❧ Learn Hebrews 11:35b–37 (NKJV). Memorize the words in **bold**.

Others were tortured, not accepting deliverance, that they might obtain a better resurrection. Still others had trial of mockings and scourgings, yes, and of chains and imprisonment. They were stoned, they were sawn in two, were tempted, were slain with the sword.

FURTHER STUDY:

❧ Research the Great Wall of China.

↻ How long is the wall? (*5,500 miles*)

↻ How tall is the Great Wall of China? (*in some places 25 feet*)

↻ How wide is the Great Wall? (*15 to 30 feet*)

↻ How long did it take to build the existing wall? (*the Ming section took about 200 years*)

↻ How was it defended? (*watch towers & forts*)

83

LESSON 65 Activity

🐦 Color the Brazilian flag using the picture in the textbook as a guide.

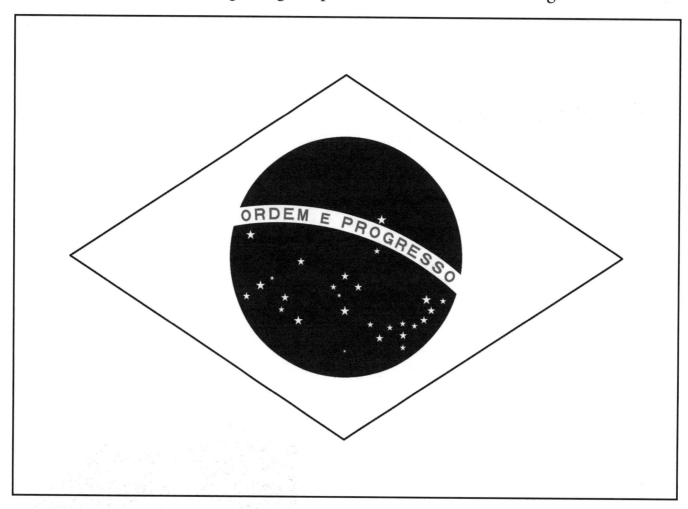

SOMETHING ELSE TO DO

🐦 Learn Galatians 3:28 (NKJV). Memorize the words in **bold**.

There is neither Jew nor Greek, there is neither slave nor free, there is neither male nor female; for **you are all one in Christ Jesus**.

LESSON 66 Activities

🐦 Go to page 114 of this *Activity Book* and find the map of the world. Locate the correct outline of Brazil, and color it green.

🐦 The Portuguese word for "Jesus" is the same as our word "Jesus"; but they pronounce it differently. Color the word "Jesus" green next to the map of Brazil on page 114 of this *Activity Book*.

SOMETHING ELSE TO DO

- Learn Matthew 6:24a (NKJV). Memorize the words in **bold**.

No one can serve two masters; for either he will hate the one and love the other, or else he will be loyal to the one and despise the other.

South America

Amazon Rainforest

FURTHER STUDY:

- Research the Amazon River.

  - How long is it? (*4,000 miles*)

  - Where does it start? (*Andes Mountains, Peru*) End? (*Atlantic Ocean, Macapa*)

- Research the Amazon Rain Forest.

  - What kinds of animals live there? (*river dolphins, Amazonian Manatee, piranha, Scarlet Macaw, black caiman, jaguar, cougar, anaconda, etc.*)

  - What is the weather like? (*rainfall 9 feet yearly, warm & humid, avg. 79° F*)

LESSON 67 Activity

- Color the British flag using the picture in the textbook as a guide.

 Memorize Hosea 14:1 (NKJV).

O Israel, return to the LORD your God, for you have stumbled because of your iniquity.

LESSON 68 Activities

 Go to page 114 of this *Activity Book* and find the map of the world. Locate the correct outline of the United Kingdom, and color it purple.

 Color the word "Jesus" purple next to the map of the United Kingdom on page 114 of the *Activity Book*.

SOMETHING ELSE TO DO

 Learn Revelation 2:4b–5a (NKJV). Memorize the words in **bold**.

[You] have left your first love. Remember therefore from where you have fallen; **repent and do the first works.**

FURTHER STUDY:

 Research John Wycliffe, John Newton, John Wesley, or George Whitefield.

  ⊃ When did they live?

  ⊃ What did they do?

 Research the Westminster Confession of Faith.

  ⊃ When was it written?

  ⊃ Get a copy and read a portion of it.

John Calvin (1509–1564)

The Westminster Confession of Faith is a Reformed confession of faith, in the Calvinist theological tradition.

UNIT 8: *Jesus, the Perfect Pilgrim*

LESSON 69 Activities

🙠 Read about this temptation in Matthew 4:8–10. What did Jesus say to Satan's attack?

🙠 Trace the second part of verse 10 of Matthew 4:

Worship the LORD your
God, and Him only you
shall serve.

🙠 Color the picture of the Little Pilgrims.

SOMETHING ELSE TO DO

ٮ Learn John 1:1–3 (NKJV). Memorize the words in **bold**.

In the beginning was the Word, and the Word was with God, and the Word was God. He was in the beginning with God. **All things were made through Him, and without Him nothing was made that was made**.

ٮ Learn the meaning of the vocabulary word "worship." Add the word **worship** to your Memory Game.

ٮ Read about the other two temptations of Jesus in Matthew 4:1–11.

⊃ How did Satan try to tempt Jesus?

⊃ How did Jesus respond to each temptation?

⊃ How can Jesus help you when you are being tempted?

LESSON 70 Activity

ٮ In *Little Pilgrims in God's World* you have learned how Jesus likens Himself to light and living water. Color the picture.

SOMETHING ELSE TO DO

- Memorize John 1:4–5 (NKJV).

  In Him was life, and the life was the light of men. And the light shines in the darkness, and the darkness did not comprehend it.

FURTHER STUDY:

- Look up the following passages and discuss how Jesus is:

  - the Word—John 1:1, 2

  - the Living Water—John 4:7–15

  - the Bread of Life—John 6:30–35

  - the Light of the World—John 8:12

  - the Gate—John 10:7–9

  - the Good Shepherd—John 10:11–16

  - the Vine—John 15:1–8

  - the Alpha and Omega—Revelation 21:6

Cut outs ahead!

Six Days of Creation

DAY 1

DAY 2

DAY 3

DAY 4

DAY 5

DAY 6

DAY 7

And on the seventh day God ended his work ...and he rested... Genesis 2:2

Directions:

After you have finished coloring all the pictures (Lesson 17), remove this page from the book. Cut along the dotted lines, and glue or tape the pieces of paper together to form a timeline.

Bible verses ahead!

Lesson 13—Memorize Verse

Then God said, "Let the earth bring forth the living creature."

Genesis 1:24 (NKJV)

Lesson 14—Memorize Verse

And God made the beast of the earth ..., cattle ..., and everything that creeps on the earth.

Genesis 1:25 (NKJV)

Lesson 15—Memorize Verse

Then God said, "Let Us make man in Our image, according to Our likeness...."

Genesis 1:26 (NKJV)

Lesson 16—Memorize Verse

Cursed is the ground for your sake; in toil you shall eat of it all the days of your life.

Genesis 3:17b (NKJV)

Lesson 17—Memorize Verse

Then God blessed the seventh day and sanctified it, ... He rested from all His work.

Genesis 2:3 (NKJV)

Lesson 18—Memorize Verse

Have dominion over the fish ..., over the birds ..., and over every living thing ...."

Genesis 1:28 (NKJV)

Lesson 19—Memorize Verse

And the LORD God said, "It is not good that man should be alone; I will make him a helper."

Genesis 2:18 (NKJV)

Lesson 20—Memorize Verse

And the LORD God commanded ..., "Of the tree of the knowledge of good and evil you shall not eat."

Genesis 2:16-17 (NKJV)

Lesson 21—Memorize Verse

Watch and pray, lest you enter into temptation.

Matthew 26:41 (NKJV)

Lesson 22—Memorize Verse

She took of its fruit and ate. She also gave to her husband with her, and he ate.

Genesis 3:6 (NKJV)

Lesson 23—Memorize Verse

For as in Adam all die.

1 Corinthians 15:22a (NKJV)

Lesson 24—Memorize Verse

And [God] said, "... Have you eaten from the tree of which I commanded you that you should not eat?

Genesis 3:11b (NKJV)

Bible Memory

Bible Memory

Bible Memory

Bible Memory

Bible Memory

Bible Memory

Bible Memory

Bible Memory

Bible Memory

Bible Memory

Bible Memory

Bible Memory

◯ Lesson 25—Memorize Verse

He shall bruise your head, and you shall bruise His heel.

Genesis 3:15 (NKJV)

◯ Lesson 26—Memorize Verse

Also for Adam and his wife the LORD God made tunics of skin, and clothed them.

Genesis 3:21 (NKJV)

◯ Lesson 27—Memorize Verse

For God so loved the world that He gave His only begotten Son, that whoever believes in Him should not perish, but have everlasting life.

John 3:16 (NKJV)

◯ Lesson 28—Memorize Verse

What shall we say then? Shall we continue in sin that grace may abound? Certainly not!

Romans 6:1–2 (NKJV)

◯ Lesson 29—Memorize Verse

For whoever does the will of God is My brother and My sister and mother.

Mark 3:35 (NKJV)

◯ Lesson 30—Memorize Verse

You shall love the LORD your God with all your heart, with all your soul, and with all your mind. ... [and] You shall love your neighbor as yourself

Matthew 22:37, 39 (NKJV)

◯ Lesson 31—Memorize Verse

He saw the Spirit of God descending ... upon Him. And ... a voice came from heaven, saying, "This is My beloved Son, in whom I am well pleased."

Matthew 3:16–17 (NKJV)

◯ Lesson 32—Memorize Verse

But the Helper, the Holy Spirit, whom the Father will send in My name, He will teach you all things.

John 14:26 (NKJV)

◯ Lesson 33—Memorize Verse

Let each one of you ... so love his own wife as himself, and let the wife see that she respects her husband.

Ephesians 5:33 (NKJV)

◯ Lesson 34—Memorize Verse

Husbands, love your wives, just as Christ also loved the church and gave Himself for her.

Ephesians 5:25 (NKJV)

◯ Lesson 35—Memorize Verse

Fathers, do not provoke your children to wrath, but bring them up in the training and admonition of the Lord.

Ephesians 6:4 (NKJV)

◯ Lesson 36—Memorize Verse

For whom the Lord loves He chastens, and scourges every son whom He receives.

Hebrews 12:6 (NKJV)

Bible Memory

Bible Memory

Bible Memory

Bible Memory

Bible Memory

Bible Memory

Bible Memory

Bible Memory

Bible Memory

Bible Memory

Bible Memory

Bible Memory

Lesson 37—Memorize Verse

But Jesus ... said, "Let the children come to Me, and do not forbid them; for of such is the kingdom of God."

Luke 18:16 (NKJV)

Lesson 38—Memorize Verse

Be strong and of good courage, do not fear nor be afraid of them; for the LORD your God, He is the One who goes with you. He will not leave you nor forsake you.

Deuteronomy 31:6 (NKJV)

Lesson 39—Memorize Verse

Honor your father and your mother, that your days may be long upon the land which the LORD your God is giving you.

Exodus 20:12 (NKJV)

Lesson 40—Memorize Verse

I have no greater joy than to hear that my children walk in truth.

3 John 1:4 (NKJV)

Lesson 41—Memorize Verse

Now faith is the substance of things hoped for, the evidence of things not seen.

Hebrews 11:1 (NKJV)

Lesson 42—Memorize Verse

These all died in faith, ... and confessed that they were strangers and pilgrims on the earth"

Hebrews 11:13 (NKJV)

Lesson 43—Memorize Verse

Go therefore and make disciples of all the nations, ... and lo, I am with you always, even to the end of the age.

Matthew 28:19a, 20b (NKJV)

Lesson 44—Memorize Verse

Repent, and let every one of you be baptized in the name of Jesus Christ for the remission of sins; and you shall receive the gift of the Holy Spirit.

Acts 2:38 (NKJV)

Lesson 45—Memorize Verse

Then Paul ... received all who came to him, preaching the kingdom of God.

Acts 28:30–31 (NKJV)

Lesson 46—Memorize Verse

For as the body is one and has many members, ... so also is Christ.

1 Corinthians 12:12 (NKJV)

Lesson 47—Memorize Verse

Remember the Sabbath day, to keep it holy.

Exodus 20:8 (NKJV)

Lesson 48—Memorize Verse

The LORD blessed the Sabbath day and hallowed it.

Exodus 20:11b (NKJV)

Bible Memory

Bible Memory

Bible Memory

Bible Memory

Bible Memory

Bible Memory

Bible Memory

Bible Memory

Bible Memory

Bible Memory

Bible Memory

Bible Memory

Lesson 49—Memorize Verse

Let everything that has breath praise the LORD. Praise the LORD!

Psalm 150:6 (NKJV)

Lesson 50—Memorize Verse

But I say to you, love your enemies ... and pray for those who ... persecute you.

Matthew 5:44 (NKJV)

Lesson 51—Memorize Verse

For there is no authority except from God, and the authorities that exist are appointed by God.

Romans 13:1 (NKJV)

Lesson 52—Memorize Verse

For rulers are not a terror to good works, but to evil.

Romans 13:3a (NKJV)

Lesson 53—Memorize Verse

Seek the peace of the city where I have caused you to be carried away captive, and pray to the LORD for it; for in its peace you will have peace.

Jeremiah 29:7 (NKJV)

Lesson 54—Memorize Verse

In My Father's house are many mansions; if it were not so, I would have told you. I go to prepare a place for you.

John 14:2 (NKJV)

Lesson 55—Memorize Verse

Blessed are the peacemakers, for they shall be called sons of God.

Matthew 5:9 (NKJV)

Lesson 56—Memorize Verse

You shall love your neighbor as yourself.

Matthew 22:39b (NKJV)

Lesson 57—Memorize Verse

Go therefore and make disciples of all the nations, baptizing them in the name of the Father and of the Son and of the Holy Spirit.

Matthew 28:19 (NKJV)

Lesson 58—Memorize Verse

And let him who thirsts come. Whoever desires, let him take the water of life freely.

Revelation 22:17 (NKJV)

Lesson 59—Memorize Verse

And again I say to you, it is easier for a camel to go through the eye of a needle than for a rich man to enter the kingdom of God.

Matthew 19:24 (NKJV)

Lesson 60—Memorize Verse

Lay up for yourselves treasures in heaven, where neither moth nor rust destroys and where thieves do not break in and steal.

Matthew 6:20 (NKJV)

Bible Memory

Bible Memory

Bible Memory

Bible Memory

Bible Memory

Bible Memory

Bible Memory

Bible Memory

Bible Memory

Bible Memory

Bible Memory

Bible Memory

◯ Lesson 61—Memorize Verse

When Israel was a child, I loved him, and out of Egypt I called My son.

Hosea 11:1 (NKJV)

◯ Lesson 62—Memorize Verse

You shall have no other gods before Me.

Exodus 20:3 (NKJV)

◯ Lesson 63—Memorize Verse

Remember the word that I said to you, "A servant is not greater than his master." If they persecuted Me, they will also persecute you.

John 15:20 (NKJV)

◯ Lesson 64—Memorize Verse

Others were tortured, not accepting deliverance, that they might obtain a better resurrection.

Hebrews 11:35b (NKJV)

◯ Lesson 65—Memorize Verse

You are all one in Christ Jesus.

Galatians 3:28 (NKJV)

◯ Lesson 66—Memorize Verse

No one can serve two masters; for either he will hate the one and love the other.

Matthew 6:24a (NKJV)

◯ Lesson 67—Memorize Verse

O Israel, return to the LORD your God, for you have stumbled because of your iniquity.

Hosea 14:1 (NKJV)

◯ Lesson 68—Memorize Verse

[You] have left your first love.... Repent and do the first works.

Revelation 2:4b, 5a (NKJV)

◯ Lesson 69—Memorize Verse

All things were made through Him, and without Him nothing was made that was made.

John 1:3 (NKJV)

◯ Lesson 70—Memorize Verse

In Him was life, and the life was the light of men. And the light shines in the darkness, and the darkness did not comprehend it.

John 1:4–5 (NKJV)

Vocabulary ahead!

_____

Bible Memory

_____

Bible Memory

_____

Bible Memory

_____

Bible Memory

_____

Bible Memory

_____

Bible Memory

_____

Bible Memory

_____

Bible Memory

_____

Bible Memory

_____

Bible Memory

heaven	where God lives heaven
cultivate	to plant things and take care of those things that were planted cultivate
tempted	to want to do something you were told not to do tempted
grace	not getting the punishment you deserve grace
substitute	someone who takes the place of someone else substitute
trust	believing in something no matter what trust

Memory Game	*Memory Game*
Memory Game	*Memory Game*
Memory Game	*Memory Game*
Memory Game	*Memory Game*
Memory Game	*Memory Game*
Memory Game	*Memory Game*

selfish	to care about yourself more than others
	selfish

bride	another name for wife
	bride

discipline	to correct the behavior of someone
	discipline

honor	to obey and respect
	honor

faith	believing in something you cannot see
	faith

martyr	someone who dies because of his or her belief in God
	martyr

Memory Game	*Memory Game*
Memory Game	*Memory Game*
Memory Game	*Memory Game*
Memory Game	*Memory Game*
Memory Game	*Memory Game*
Memory Game	*Memory Game*

mercy	like forgiveness mercy
government	a person or group of people that rules over another group of people government
apostle	a disciple who Jesus especially called to serve as a preacher and missionary apostle
continent	one of the world's seven large, continuous expanses of land continent
freedom	being allowed to do things and not having to do what you do not want to do freedom
worship	loving someone or something with all your heart worship

Memory Game

Memory Game

Memory Game

Memory Game

Memory Game

Memory Game

Memory Game

Memory Game

Memory Game

Memory Game

Memory Game

Memory Game

耶穌

CHINA

Beijing ★

○Hong Kong

EGYPT

Cairo ☆

ria

Africa

Pacific
Ocean

Indian
Ocean

You may remove pages 114 and 115
from the *Activity Book*, cut off the
white edge on the right-hand side of
page 114, line up the two sheets of
paper so the map is aligned prop-
erly, and tape them together.

The United States of America

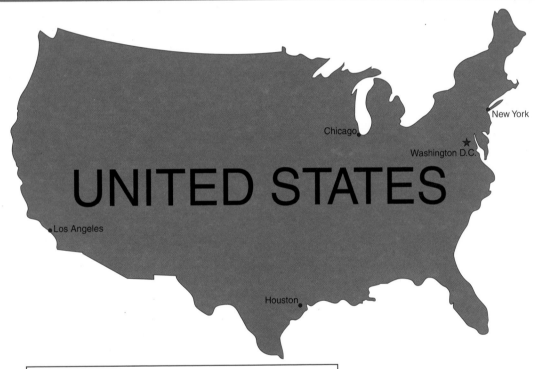

UNITED STATES

New York

Chicago

Washington D.C.

Los Angeles

Houston

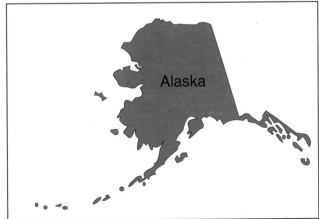

Alaska

Hawaii

Egypt—Arab Republic of Egypt

Alexandria ★ Cairo

EGYPT

Aswan

China—People's Republic of China

Beijing ★

CHINA

○ Hong Kong

Brazil—Federative Republic of Brazil

BRAZIL

★
Brasilia

● Rio de Janeiro

The United Kingdom
of Great Britain and Northern Ireland

Edinburgh

NORTHERN
IRELAND

UNITED KINGDOM

London ★